Barry Appleby's
The GAMBOLS
BOOK Nº 48
by
Roger Mahoney

sssssss

ublished by
Pedigree BOOKS

he Old Rectory
atford Lane, Exeter
evon EX2 4PS

nder licence from Express Newspapers Ltd. Printed in the UK.

£6.99
(GA48)

D0189371

THIS YEAR WE DISOVERED THE COMFORTS OF RELAXING IN OUR OWN CONSERVATORY

SHOPPING IS ONE OF GAYES' FAVOURITE PASTIMES ~ UNFORTUNATELY FOR GEORGE

NOWADAYS IT SEEMS THAT EVERYONE
HAS TO GIVE A ONE HUNDRED AND TEN
PERCENT EFFORT TO SURVIVE ~
GEORGE IS WORKING ON IT

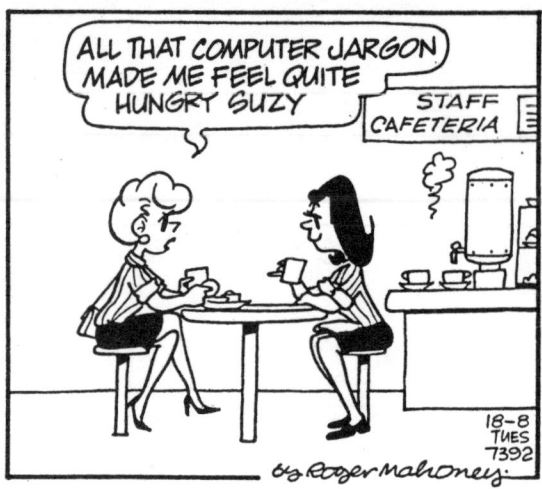

IT'S FUNNY — BUT GAYE STILL CAN'T SEE
THE FUN IN HELPING GEORGE RESTORE
THAT VINTAGE CAR

WE LOVE HAVING MIGGY AND FLIVVER TO
STAY ~ PREFERABLY DURING FINE WEATHER

GEORGE FINDS HIS RIDE-ON MOWER
TOO MUCH FUN TO ACTUALLY MOW ANY LAWN

WE ALWAYS ENJOY A
RELAXING EVENING IN FRONT
OF THE TELEVISION

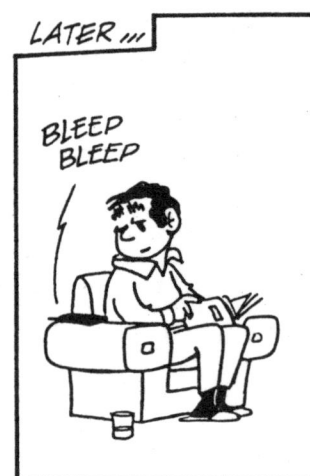

IF ONLY CARS WERE NOT AN ESSENTIAL PART OF DAILY LIFE !

LUCKY FOR US WE'VE ALWAYS BEEN ABLE
TO SEE THE FUNNY SIDE OF LIFE

GEORGE AND GAYE REALLY ENJOY
BROWSING AROUND ANTIQUE FAIRS

SUN SEA SAND AND SURPRISES ~
THERE'S NOTHING LIKE A HOLIDAY
AWAY FROM IT ALL

GEORGE NEVER HAS THE LAST WORD AS
FAR AS COLOURS ARE CONCERNED

THERE'S NEVER A DULL MOMENT WHEN
MIGGY AND FLIVVER COME TO STAY WITH US

THERE ARE THE ODD OCCASIONS WHEN GEORGE
ACTUALLY ENJOYS SHOPPING AT THE SUPERMARKET

CHRISTMAS IS OVER AND DONE WITH ～ SO
IT'S BACK TO WORK AND RARING TO GO

..., SO AS ANOTHER YEAR FLIES BY AND THE NEW MILLENNIUM IS UPON US ~ WE ARE LOOKING FORWARD TO MEETING YOU AGAIN TOMORROW MORNING AND EVERY DAY IN THE EXPRESS ~ 'BYE FOR NOW